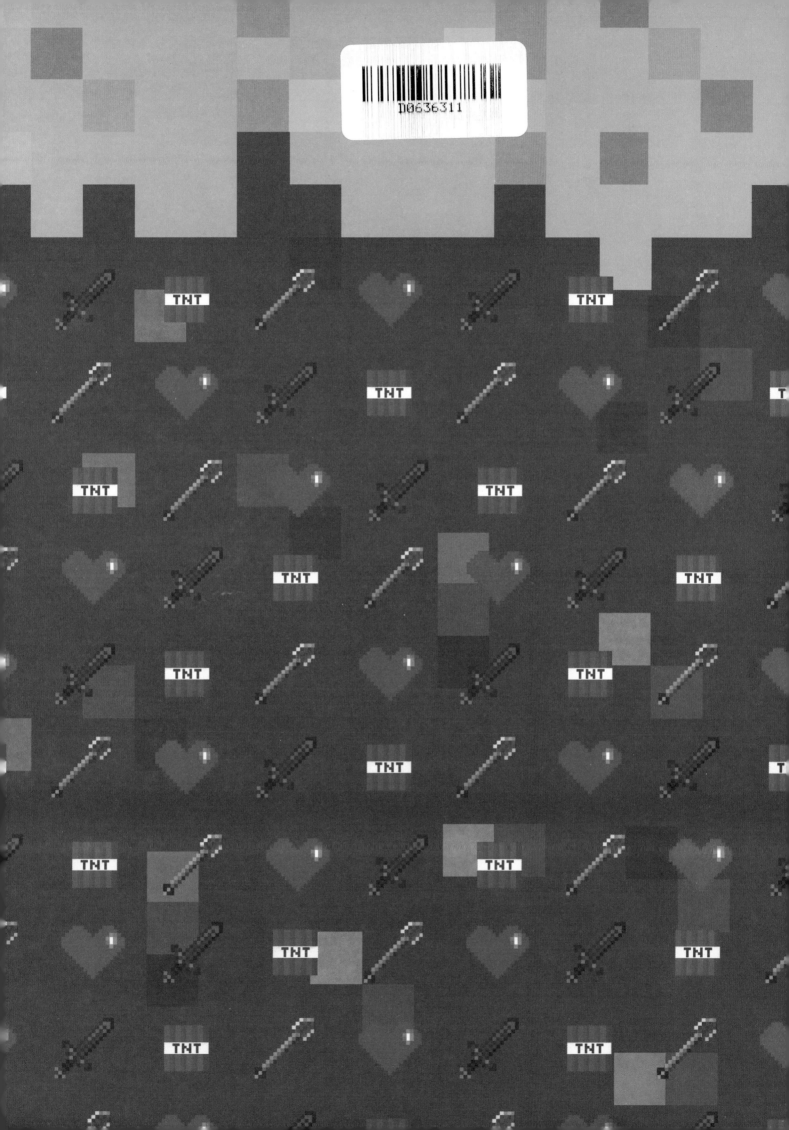

D0636311

Minecrafters Unite

A CENTUM BOOK 978-1-913399-84-9

Published in Great Britain by Centum Books Ltd

This edition published 2020

1 3 5 7 9 10 8 6 4 2

© Centum Books 2020

Illustrated by Caroline Martin

Shutterstock.com

We have produced this "100% Unofficial Minecrafters Unite" book independently
from Mojang Synergies AB, the owner of the MINECRAFT® registered trade marks.
To be completely clear, this book has not been authorised, approved, licensed,
sanctioned or sponsored by Mojang Synergies AB. Mojang Synergies AB owns all
rights in the MINECRAFT products and trade marks.

No part of this publication may be reproduced, stored in a retrieval system,
or transmitted in any form or by any means, electronic, mechanical, photocopying,
recording or otherwise, without the prior permission of the publishers.

Centum Books Ltd, 20 Devon Square, Newton Abbot, Devon, TQ12 2HR, UK

books@centumbooksltd.co.uk

CENTUM BOOKS Limited Reg. No. 07641486

A CIP catalogue record for this book is available from the British Library.

Printed in China.

100% UNOFFICIAL

MINECRAFTERS UNITE

TNT

TNT

TNT

TNT

TNT

TNT

TNT

TNT

TNT

TNT

THIS BOOK BELONGS TO

Georgia lilly Zante

CONTENTS

BOOM BOOM

Use this blank template to create your character's look.

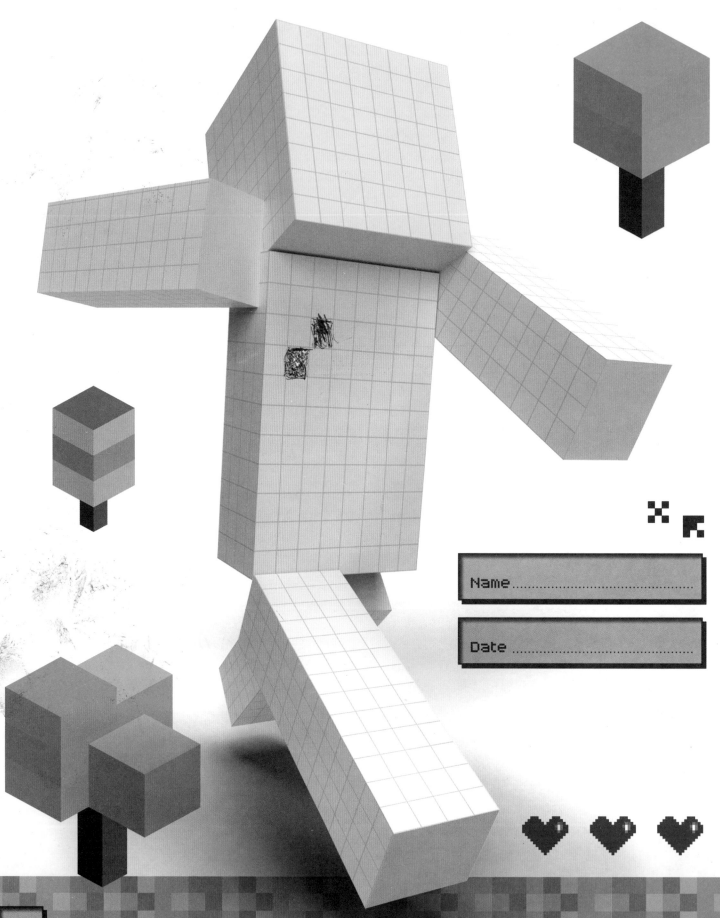

Name...

Date...

FAVOURITE HAIR COLOUR

....

....

FAVOURITE HAIRSTYLE

....

....

FAVOURITE JACKET

....

....

FAVOURITE TEE SHIRT

....

....

FAVOURITE TROUSERS

....

....

FAVOURITE FOOTWEAR

....

....

LOOT AND TREASURE GUIDE
SHIPWRECKS

THERE ARE THREE TYPES OF CHEST IN A SHIPWRECK:

MAP CHESTS contain paper, feathers, books, buried treasure maps, empty maps, compasses and clocks.

SUPPLY CHESTS contain wheat, rotten flesh, paper, carrot, coal, potato, poisonous potato, gunpowder, pumpkin, enchanted leather clothes (all pieces) and TNT.

TREASURE CHESTS contain iron nuggets, iron ingots, lapis lazuli, emeralds, gold nuggets, gold ingots, bottles o' enchanting and diamonds.

CUSTOMISE A PICKAXE!

You'll be hard pressed to find a more useful tool than the trusty pickaxe. **Using your design skills, turn this pixel pickaxe into your own unique item.**

Why not decorate the pickaxe using the theme of your favourite biome?

TOP TIP! >>>>>>>>>>>>>>>>>>>>>>>>>>>>>>>>

Always practise staircase mining for easy exits.

DID YOU KNOW?

You can tame a wolf with a bone!

JOKES

LOL!

HA HA

WHAT DID THE MINECRAFTER DO WHEN THEIR NINTENDO COPY OF MINECRAFT DIDN'T WORK?
He Switch-ed it!

WHAT HAPPENS TO MINECRAFTERS WHO GO ON SOCIAL MEDIA?
They get blocked!

WHAT'S A CREEPER'S FAVOURITE SUBJECT AT SCHOOL?
Hisssssssssssssssssstory!

WHERE DID THE MINECRAFTER FLY TO WHEN HE PLAYED PETER PAN IN THE SCHOOL PLAY?
Nether-land!

WHAT DO YOU GET FOR FINISHING SECOND IN THE UNDERWATER OLYMPICS?
A silver-fish medal!

WHAT DID THE CAT SAY WHEN IT WAS OVERCHARGED FOR A COPY OF MINECRAFT?
Ocelot of money!

BLOCK MAZE

Exploring is hungry work. **Find your way back to shore through this ocean maze, collecting as many fish as you can to cook on your furnace.**

START

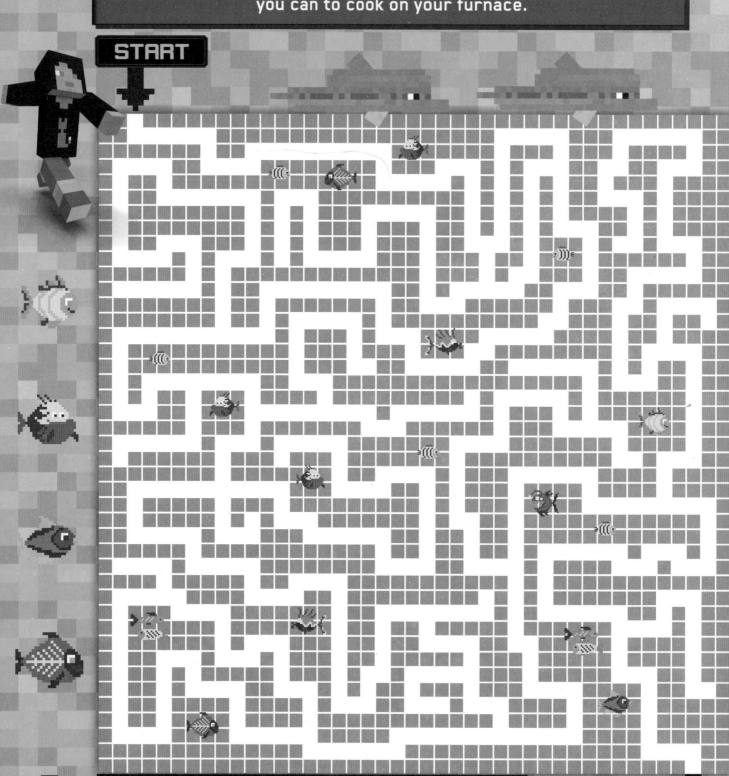

FINISH

UNDERWATER SECRETS

DOLPHIN-FRIENDLY

Dolphins will follow boats near the surface, and jump out of the water as they do. If you feed one a raw cod, it will lead you to the nearest buried treasure chest or shipwreck!

Answer on **PAGE 75**

COLOUR BLOCK CODE

The colour sequence repeats in the grid below, but there are eight errors. **Start at the top left and follow the blocks left to right, row by row, and find the errors in the code.**

SEQUENCE

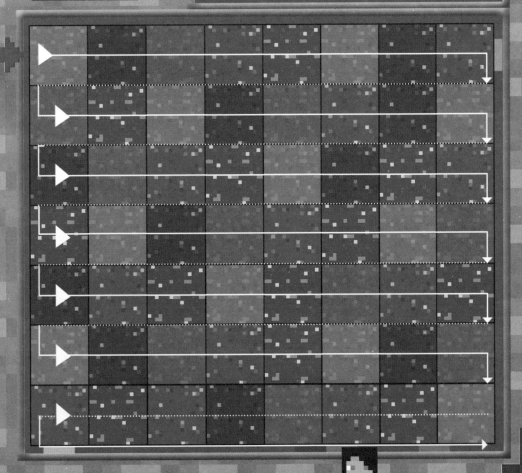

START HERE

BLOCK 'N' ROLL

DID YOU KNOW?   Sprint jumping is the fastest way to get around.

Answer on PAGE 75

EXPLORER'S CHECKLIST

Do you love going out and exploring maps? **If you do, then take these items wherever you go. You never know what the day or night will bring!**

Armour		☐
Arrows		☐
Bed		☐
Boat		☐
Bow		☐
Cobblestone		☐
Compass		☐
Cooked Food		☐
Gravel		☐
Ladders		☐

DID YOU KNOW?

Mushroom lands are found out in the ocean.

TOP TIP!

Keeping your hunger bar full will replenish your health and allow you to run, so always carry food. Cake and rabbit stew restore the most items, but cake has low saturation so your hunger will start dropping again soon after eating it, and rabbit stew takes a lot of crafting.

Cooked steak and porkchops are the best food sources. They restore 8 points of health and 12.8 points of saturation, and they stack in the inventory, so you can carry plenty!

	Map	○
	Pickaxe	○
	Raw Food	○
	Spade	○
	Sword	○
	Torches	○
	Water Bucket	○
	Wooden Planks	○

How many have you taken out with you?

What other items do you think are essential?

Other items you've found useful:

HH Ladders
....

....

....

VILLAGE VENTURES

Villages are a great source of trade for items you need or want to get rid off. Villages spawn in biomes and are themed around their surroundings. **How many villages have you come across?**

Write each one you've visited on the list below.

VILLAGES I'VE DISCOVERED:

....

....

....

....

....

....

....

....

....

....

FEATURES:

WOOD HUTS

SMALL HOUSES

LARGE HOUSES

BUTCHER'S SHOPS

LIBRARIES

FARMS

WELLS

BLACKSMITHS

CHURCHES

LAMP POSTS

ROADS

IRON GOLEMS

DID YOU KNOW? Villagers all have their own special jobs and roles to play.

TRADING TIPS

VILLAGERS LOVE EMERALDS.

Trade them for what you need. Even if a villager doesn't have something you need right now it's still good to trade because you will build a good reputation that can lead to discounts. Some villagers might try to trick you, so be a bit wary.

WATCH OUT FOR ZOMBIE VILLAGES

THERE IS A 2% CHANCE OF ONE SPAWNING.

You'll know you're entering a zombie village by the decor. No torches, lots of cobwebs and no doors are a clue – apart from the zombie villagers of course!

HEEP OUT!

Do your best impression of a zombie villager!

TOP TIP

Always use torches to stop mobs from spawning.

CREATURE CREATE

Using the grid below, colour in the pixels to create a cool creature that is found in the ocean biome.

BLOCK 'N' ROLL

Creature's name ....

LOOT AND TREASURE GUIDE
BONUS CHESTS

A bonus chest is generated at the spawn point if you tick the box during world generation. It contains loot that's useful early on: sticks, oak planks, apples, raw salmon, bread, wooden pickaxe, wooden axe, spruce log, oak log, jungle log, dark oak log, birch log, acacia log, stone pickaxe and stone axe.

UNDERWATER SECRETS

SUNKEN REMAINS

Ruins are the flooded remnants of villages from Minecraft's distant past. There are over 50 structure variants and you'll find them in the following biomes: Ocean, Cold Ocean, Frozen Ocean, Warm Ocean, Lukewarm Ocean, Deep Ocean, Deep Cold Ocean, Deep Frozen Ocean and Deep Lukewarm Ocean.

BUILD BIO

Name: ....

Spawn date: ◯ ◯ / ◯ ◯ / ◯ ◯ ◯ ◯

Survived first day?   YES ◯   NO ◯

Survived first night?   YES ◯   NO ◯

Number of hours played so far: ◯ ◯ ◯ ◯

Longest time of survival: ....

Rarest item found: ....

Rarest item crafted: ....

Furthest you've travelled: ....

STAYING ALIVE TIPS

LISTEN OUT

It's easy to focus on the stuff you can see around you, but don't forget to keep your ears open too, especially when you're underground. Listening to sounds around you is the perfect way to navigate away from danger. A zombie's moan, a skeleton's bony clink or the hiss of a creeper can all tell you danger's around, while bubbling lava or running water let you know there's a cavern – and some potential riches – close by!

DRESS FOR THE OCCASION

Always wear the best armour you can. Once you have an iron pickaxe, get some iron armour. Once you start finding diamonds, save them for diamond armour. You can't die if you can't be hurt, and wearing the strongest possible armour will take care of it. Leather armour is just for decoration – by the time you can even find enough leather to craft it, you should be well on your way to smelting ingots!

ALWAYS LOOK DOWN

Fall damage is the hardest type of damage to protect yourself against, and there's almost no way to guard against it altogether. If you have to make a long drop, aim to land in some water to avoid damage completely, while landing on a bed, hay bale or slime block will also reduce damage. What you should really do is use the sneak key near a ledge, as you can't fall while you're sneaking!

Put a tick next to each mode you've played.

- [ ] SURVIVAL
- [ ] CREATIVE
- [ ] HARDCORE
- [ ] PEACEFUL
- [ ] ADVENTURE
- [ ] SPECTATOR

BASE PLANNER

Design your ultimate survival base on these pages.
Somewhere you can hide in and also call home!

What are you going to prioritise?

Things to think about
ACCESSIBILITY / LIGHT / STORAGE / CRAFTING
FOOD SOURCE / DEFENCE / SECRETS / RESOURCES

MARKET

YOU NEED: Oak logs, stairs, oak planks, chests

Why not create a small market-style shop? Build a frame using oak, then add a roof and a back wall. Put counters alongside chests for shoppers to browse. Display cakes, plants, or any other placeable item.

Bases on stilts can work really well — why not build your base off the ground.

TOP TIP Crouch walk backwards when fighting spiders.

POTION POWER

Calling master brewers! What if you could create your own unique potion? What ingredients would you need and what would it do? **It can be funny or serious – you choose!**

Fill in the grids, then write about your new potion.

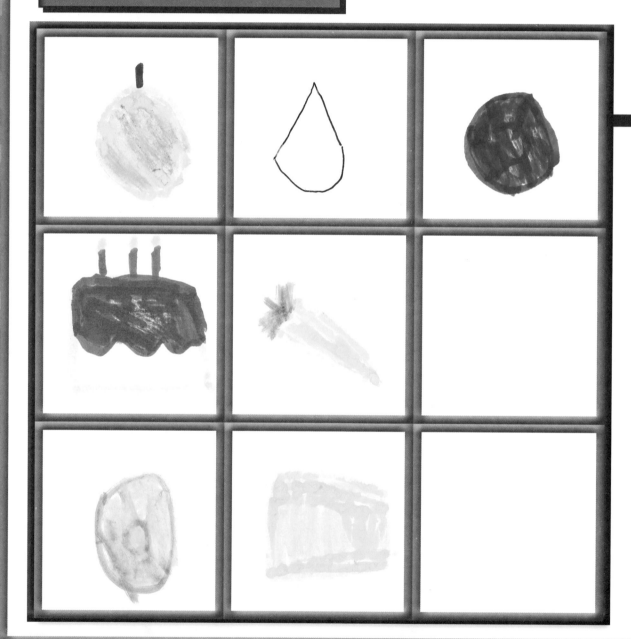

TOP TIP

STAYING ALIVE TIPS

DON'T GET INTO A FIGHT

Staying out of fights you can't win is key to long-term survival. Skill aside, fights don't become easier the more you win them. The best way to deal with this? Don't get into fights at all. This might sound obvious, but it's easy to be too confident once you've won a few. If you see three creepers in a tight space, the best way to stay alive is to get out of there as quickly as possible. You can always kill them another day!

MINECRAFT IRL!

Make some block cakes to share with your mates.
Like cupcakes, but cuboid obviously!

Always check with a grown-up before cooking or crafting!

INGREDIENTS:

SPONGE:

- 220g caster sugar
- 220g softened butter
- 4 eggs beaten
- 220g self-raising flour
- 1 ½ tsp baking powder
- 3 tbsp milk

ICING:

- 280g butter
- 200g icing sugar
- Food colouring in a theme of your choice

EQUIPMENT:

- Square baking tin
- Wooden spoon
- Spatula, palette knife or similar for decorating
- Cake slice
- Baking paper

1.
Heat oven to 190 °C/fan 170 °C/ gas 5. Butter your tin and line with non-stick baking paper.

2.
In a large bowl, make the sponge mix: beat caster sugar, softened butter, eggs, self-raising flour, baking powder and milk together until you have a smooth, soft batter.

3.
Pour batter in your tin and use a spatula or the back of a spoon to flatten the top.

4.
Bake for about 20 mins until golden and the cake springs back when pressed.

5.
Turn onto a cooling rack and leave to cool.

6.
To make the icing, beat the softened butter until smooth and creamy, then gradually add in sifted icing sugar. Divide into at least three smaller bowls. Add different amounts of one food colouring to each bowl to achieve different shades, or use different colours for each bowl.

7.
Take the bread knife and slice your cooled sponge carefully into cubes.

8.
Spread the buttercream over each block. Decorate if you wish! See the additional tip.

9.
Arrange your blocks to create a pixel picture, leave as one giant block, or simply devour on the spot! Keep in an airtight container and eat within 2 days.

DECORATION TIP:

An easy way to decorate your block cakes is to do icing faces or words. Simply cut a face or letter design out of paper to make a stencil that that will fit on top of a block cake. Hold the stencil above and shake the icing sugar over the top.

BEFORE AND AFTER

Before you started playing the game, did you have any ideas about what it would be like? How does it compare in reality?

Complete the before and after table below.

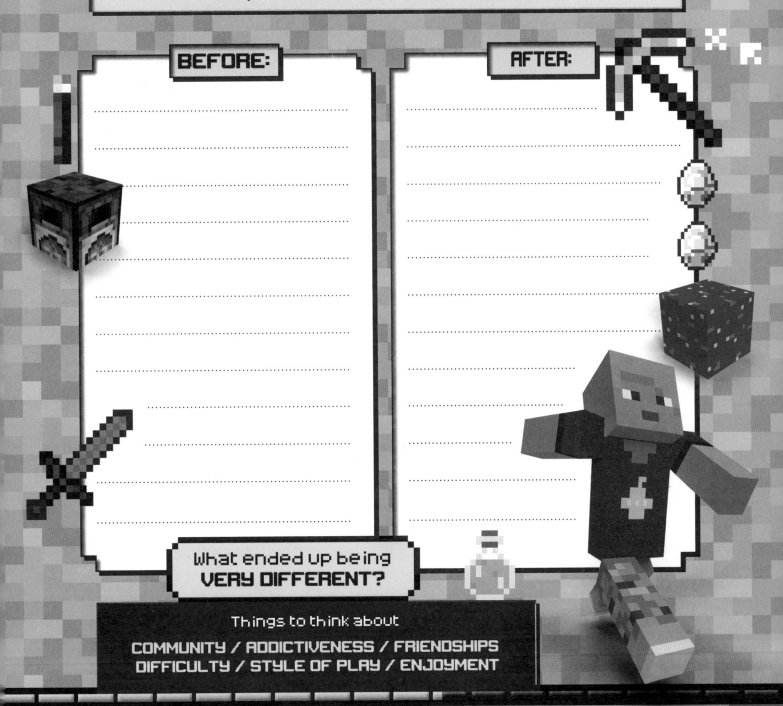

BEFORE:

AFTER:

What ended up being
VERY DIFFERENT?

Things to think about

COMMUNITY / ADDICTIVENESS / FRIENDSHIPS
DIFFICULTY / STYLE OF PLAY / ENJOYMENT

TOP TIP! >>>>>>>>>>>>>>>>>>>>>>>>>>>>

Anvils can replenish the durability of other items.

DID YOU KNOW?

Tall birch forests are really beautiful
– see if you can find this rare biome.

CHALLENGE AHOY!

Time to think about your future self! One way to become better at survival is to set challenges to help you improve and achieve your goals. Try to complete each Challenge Card.

Log your results in the table below.

Cut out the cards along the dotted line, shuffle the deck and randomly pick a challenge to attempt!

BLOCK 'N' ROLL

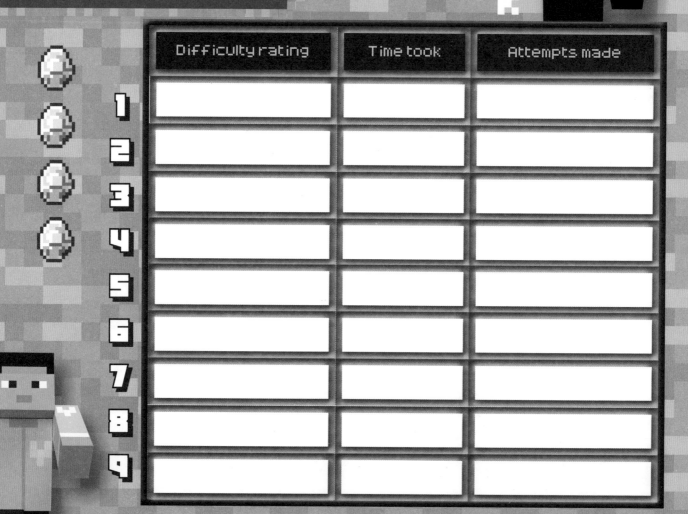

	Difficulty rating	Time took	Attempts made
1			
2			
3			
4			
5			
6			
7			
8			
9			

STAYING ALIVE TIPS

KEEP IT LIGHT ♥ ♥ ♥ ♥ ♥ ♥ ♥ ♥

Light levels matter – a lot. Light keeps hostile mobs from spawning and draws in friendly mobs, whereas the dark can hide all manner of evil creatures who are just waiting to separate you from your long-term plans. You can never have too many torches, so place them frequently and often. They don't just keep evil mobs away, they're also handy if you want to find your way back from a long journey once night falls!

1 UN BREAK ABLE

Try to play without breaking any blocks at all.

2 UN TOUCH ABLE

Try to not take any damage at all.

3 UN PROTE CTED

Try to play without wearing any armour.

4 GROUNDED

You cannot jump!

5 FRIEND

You cannot attack anyone!

6 SCARED OF HEIGHTS

You cannot travel higher than than Y=80.

7 OCEAN NO GO

You cannot enter any body of water.

8 LIGHT ALRIGHT

You cannot enter any place that does not have light.

9 ALONE

You cannot interact with anyone else.

LOOT AND TREASURE GUIDE
IGLOOS

If an igloo has a hidden basement, you'll find a chest containing any of coal, apples, wheat, gold nuggets, golden apples, rotten flesh, stone axes and emeralds.

CHALLENGE CARD

100% UNOFFICIAL
MINECRAFTERS UNITE

CHALLENGE CARD

100% UNOFFICIAL
MINECRAFTERS UNITE

CHALLENGE CARD

100% UNOFFICIAL
MINECRAFTERS UNITE

CHALLENGE CARD

100% UNOFFICIAL
MINECRAFTERS UNITE

CHALLENGE CARD

100% UNOFFICIAL
MINECRAFTERS UNITE

CHALLENGE CARD

100% UNOFFICIAL
MINECRAFTERS UNITE

CHALLENGE CARD

100% UNOFFICIAL
MINECRAFTERS UNITE

CHALLENGE CARD

100% UNOFFICIAL
MINECRAFTERS UNITE

CHALLENGE CARD

100% UNOFFICIAL
MINECRAFTERS UNITE

DID YOU KNOW?
Find a bamboo forest and you will likely find pandas!

TOP TIPS

If you were telling a friend about the game and they had never played before, what top 5 tips would you share with them?

Knowledge is BLOCK power!

1 ....

....

....

2 ....

....

....

3 ....

....

....

4 ....

....

....

5 ....

....

....

TOP TIP | Kelp is an awesome food source, as well as fuel.

CROSSWORD CHALLENGE

Complete this block-tastic crossword challenge.

3 Down: h e l m e t

Answer on PAGE 75

ACROSS
2. Regions in the world.
5. Represents your health.
6. Use to smelt in crafting.
8. The mode that has a limitless supply of blocks.
9. The point you return to when you die in the game.

DOWN
1. Used to travel between realms.
3. Armour you wear on your head.
4. The final layer in the game.
7. The first tool you will likely make and use.
9. Texture placed on an avatar for customisation.

Fancy a challenge? Set yourself a five-minute timer.

TOP TIP
Make safety doors and safes for extra protection.

32

MINING MATHS

Every icon has a value, can you work each one and solve the final problem? **Fill in the icon answer values below to help.**

DID YOU KNOW?

You can build good relationships with villagers through trading.

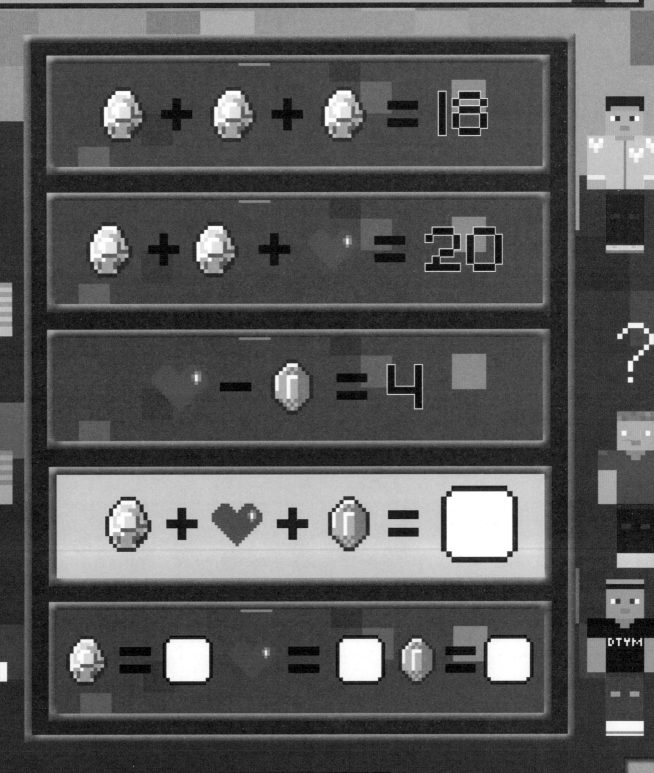

WHAT AM I?

Use your crafting knowledge and solve these puzzles to work out what the objects are.

1 I GROW IN THE GROUND AND CAN GROW VERY TALL.

You chop me down to craft your first tool.

I'M A .... BLOCK.

2 I'M SHINY AND GREEN, YOU FIND ME DOWN BELOW.

Trade me in villages wherever you go.

I'M AN ....

3 I'M AN ORE SO USEFUL YOU'LL NEED LOTS OF ME.

you can find me in the ground, but mine carefully.

I'M .... ORE.

4 I'M SHINY AND YELLOW LIKE THE SUN.

You'll find me deep down at layer 31.

I'M..................... ORE.

Answer on PAGE 75

MINI BUILDS

BATHTUB

YOU NEED: Trapdoors, buckets of water, tripwire hooks

Place the trapdoors (birch ones look best, but you can use any kind) on the floor, then open them so they stand up to create the edge of the bath. Fill the inside with water and use tripwire hooks as "taps".

BLOCK MAZE

Collect diamonds as you mine your way through
this maze, back to your torch.

FINISH

START

TOP
TIP
Always keeps lots of iron tools in circulation.

Answer on PAGE 75

OCEAN TRICKS AND TIPS

Have you explored underwater yet?
Here are some tips to improve your play.

FISH ARE A ONE HIT KILL WITH A STONE SWORD.

Items float, including dead fish, for easy collection.

KELP CAN BE SMELTED TO MAKE DRIED KELP, WHICH CAN BE THEN BE SMELTED INTO BLOCKS TO SMELT OTHER ITEMS.

DRIED HELP IS ALSO A GREAT FOOD SOURCE.

Boats are recommended for picking up items and for speedy exploration.

Bring a shield to protect yourself against hostiles especially those armed with tridents.

WHEN YOU DIE YOUR ITEMS FLOAT TO THE SURFACE.

LOOK OUT FOR SHIPWRECHS AND OCEAN RUINS – YOU CAN SPOT THEIR LIGHTS AND OBVIOUS SHAPES AS YOU LOOK TOWARDS THE HORIZON.

UNDERWATER SECRETS

NOT–SO–SUNKEN REMAINS 🥚🥚🥚🥚🥚🥚🥚🥚🥚

You can occasionally find ruins above ground – they can spawn on beaches, which makes them a lot easier to find and explore. You could even try rebuilding them!

TERRACOTTA ARMY

As of the Village & Pillage update, purple glazed terracotta appears in certain underwater ruins, and it's the only place you can find glazed terracotta. If you want to see another colour, you'll have to craft it!

HOLD SHIFT ON A MAGMA BLOCK TO BREATHE THE BUBBLE COLUMN.

HOSTILES WILL ALWAYS SPAWN AT RUINS.

MARK TREASURE YOU'VE LOOTED USING COLUMNS SO YOU KNOW NOT TO LOOK THERE AGAIN.

BIG OCEAN RUINS ARE LIKELY TO HAVE GOLDEN NUGGETS.

YOU CAN ALSO FIND BURIED TREASURE MAPS THAT YOU CAN USE TO FIND ADDITIONAL LOOT.

Magma blocks kill fish – find a few of them together and you will likely find a lot of dead fish too.

Shipwrecks typically have three chests containing minor loot to find, buried treasure maps and main loot including diamonds.

DOLPHINS CAN HELP YOU SWIM FASTER, AND EVEN LEAD YOU TO RUINS OR OCEAN TREASURE.

BURIED TREASURE IS ALWAYS UNDER SAND.

Ocean ruins will have treasure chests. Hopefully you won't have to dig too much to find one.

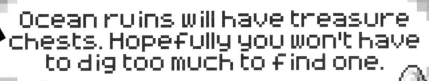

SPOT THE DIFFERENCE

Can you find and circle 10 differences between picture A and picture B? **Some are tricky so look closely!**

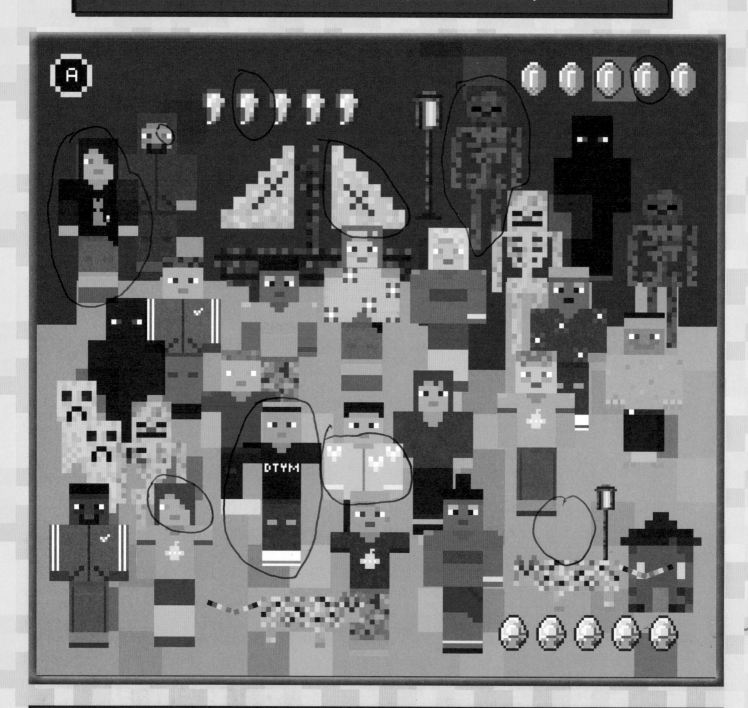

DID YOU KNOW? >>>>>>>>>>>>>>>>>>

Treasure maps can be found in ocean temples and shipwrecks.

DID YOU KNOW?

You can tame a Polar bear with raw fish!

CASTLE CREATE

Using the grid below, colour in the
pixels to create a creepy castle.

HEEP
OUT!

40

MINI BUILDS

SPOOKY GATES

YOU NEED:
Iron bars, spruce doors, torches, stone blocks

Building gates this way, with high gateposts and iron railings, makes them look more imposing – perfect for graveyards, haunted houses or old mansions.

GRAVE

YOU NEED:
Sign, polished andesite, torch, chests

Dig two blocks down and two across, and place a double chest in the open pit for a "coffin". Cover it with andesite, then use another andesite block with a torch and sign attached as the headstone. You can write anyone's name you like.

STATUE

YOU NEED:
Slabs, armour, armour stand, mob head

Build a plinth using slabs, put an armour stand on top, then hang the armour and head on the stand. You can swap one of the slabs for a sign if you want space to explain who the statue is!

LOOT AND TREASURE GUIDE
STRONGHOLDS

The size of strongholds means there are lots of items to find and three different types of chest, depending on the rooms in the stronghold. You can expect to find a good number of chests in any stronghold you visit!

Altar chests contain redstone, bread, iron ingots, apples, gold ingots, ender pearls, diamonds, iron pickaxes, iron armour (all pieces), iron swords, golden apples, saddles, diamond horse armour, gold horse armour, iron horse armour and enchanted books.

In libraries, the chests contain just a few items, but they're very uncommon: paper, books, enchanted books, compasses and empty maps.

Finally, storeroom chests can contain coal, redstone, bread, iron ingots, apples, gold ingots, enchanted books and iron pickaxes.

ALL ABOUT COMMUNITY

What a great community you are part of! **Write down your favourite resource links below so you can keep track of where you find all your BEST survival tips and favourite fellow player info.**

FAVOURITE PLAYERS:

....
....
....

FAVOURITE GROUPS:

....
....
....

FAVOURITE THREADS:

....
....
....

FAVOURITE YOUTUBE CHANNELS:

....
....
....

FAVOURITE STREAMERS:

....
....
....

FAVOURITE BOOKS:

....
....
....

MINI BUILDS

HOT TUB

YOU NEED: Lava, water, glass blocks, stairs, levers

Dig down two blocks and place some lava blocks in the bottom of your pit. Cover them with glass blocks to make a see-through floor, then surround that with stairs. Fill the inside with water, then attach levers nearby to look like water taps. Voilà: one heated pool!

PATIO SET

YOU NEED: Quartz stairs, carpet, fence posts, sandstone, slabs

Make your furniture white to resemble garden furniture. A checkerboard pattern made using sandstone and stone slabs will look better than a single design on its own.

43

BLOCK BY BLOCK

Find all the items in this ENORMOUS wordsearch.

Word list:
- ARMOUR
- BIOME
- BLOCK
- BUILD
- CHEST
- DIAMOND
- FURNACE
- GHOST
- GOLD
- LAVA
- LLAMA
- PANDA
- PICKAXE
- PIG
- PORTAL
- POTION
- SHEEP
- SKELETON
- SPAWN
- SURVIVAL
- SWORD
- WOLF
- ZOMBIE

M	L	G	C	H	Y	J	T	T	V	S	P	
Z	U	I	H	O	Y	W	T	A	D	Z	Z	
F	I	W	H	B	O	T	O	E	N	G	J	
P	F	B	G	M	Z	I	Q	R	R	A	S	
X	U	C	C	H	E	S	T	D	W	Y	H	
A	R	M	O	U	R	N	M	F	T	C	G	
F	N	J	G	E	B	H	J	H	N	M	T	
N	A	A	B	L	O	C	K	L	J	U	T	
T	C	H	M	W	T	G	Q	P	W	Q	Z	
V	E	P	C	D	I	H	E	J	G	R	J	
Y	H	W	Q	C	L	O	X	J	O	P	K	
F	I	L	P	L	H	S	X	O	L	N	D	
W	S	S	L	V	I	T	T	D	D	Y	I	
R	M	K	I	L	F	B	S	B	B	J	A	
L	U	E	P	J	A	X	G	I	U	I	M	
I	U	N	Q	V	N	M	L	O	I	Q	O	
O	G	J	A	Y	Z	N	A	M	L	V	N	
L	C	L	D	V	G	M	V	E	D	G	D	

LOOT AND TREASURE GUIDE
END CITIES

The chests in End cities are very hard to get to and only accessible very late in the game, so they **have the best loot by far.** You can expect to see gold ingots, iron ingots, beetroot seeds, diamonds, emeralds, enchanted diamond armour (all pieces), enchanted diamond pickaxes, shovels and swords, enchanted iron armour (all pieces), enchanted iron pickaxes, shovels and swords, saddles, iron horse armour, golden horse armour and diamond horse armour.

The enchantments on enchanted items are usually very high – the same as you'd receive for a Level 39 enchantment, which is higher than it's possible to even make using an enchantment table (they're capped at Level 30!).

Look left, right, up, down, diagonally, forwards and backwards!

F	N	U	K	H	D	E	R	Y	O	P	B	U	A	T	G	L	W
B	L	U	A	D	C	Z	R	A	E	E	O	R	W	H	V	S	M
O	U	B	F	E	C	W	D	E	V	T	G	N	H	M	C	Q	S
G	G	Y	E	H	S	G	H	A	F	C	O	C	M	W	O	L	F
H	K	M	V	C	W	S	B	O	U	I	V	T	Y	L	Q	I	Y
P	N	M	A	P	H	X	M	L	T	R	I	U	W	N	U	P	E
V	E	B	Y	E	M	V	A	O	B	M	P	C	P	O	V	I	V
P	L	W	T	B	N	V	P	I	C	K	A	X	E	W	Q	J	G
I	D	H	W	S	I	Y	N	D	L	E	B	Q	I	N	U	A	U
G	U	W	S	V	O	O	K	Y	K	Q	R	E	H	X	A	Y	J
H	Q	N	R	Q	T	W	V	G	Z	O	M	B	I	E	J	D
A	K	U	Z	E	N	A	G	D	Q	N	H	Y	E	P	H	T	O
D	S	Q	L	I	Y	A	D	O	T	N	P	N	S	J	J	J	D
S	N	E	G	R	J	R	X	V	B	Q	O	A	P	A	N	D	A
Q	K	V	G	E	O	C	Y	G	M	X	R	Y	A	Z	M	N	M
S	Q	H	U	W	Z	C	U	H	Y	E	T	X	W	K	D	M	B
S	G	T	S	U	O	E	U	A	N	O	A	F	N	H	F	W	U
D	Y	V	C	N	V	G	L	M	H	J	L	C	G	T	F	U	F

LOOT AND TREASURE GUIDE
NETHER FORTRESSES

Chests in the Nether have lots of great loot, which is no surprise given how hard it is to get it home safely! You can find gold ingots, Nether wart, iron ingots, diamonds, saddles, gold horse armour, obsidian, iron horse armour, flint and steel, golden chestplate, golden sword and diamond horse armour.

Answer on PAGE 75

ALL ABOUT BIOMES

There are over 60 biomes to discover in the game. That's a lot! How many have you ventured into? **Let's break down the main biomes you can find.**

There are five main types of biomes, Lush, Snowy, Cold, Dry, and Ocean. Within these are variations and even sub variations. Let's explore a few of them.

LUSH:

PLAINS:

Iconic grass blocks. Low hills. Not many trees or flowers. Watch out for cave openings in the ground. Lava pools are often found here. You'll be able to get yourself a horse – yee-hah!

FOREST:

So much wood! A crafter's paradise. You'll also find flowers for dyes and mushrooms for cooking. Not the best place to be at night if you don't have a shelter.

ROOFED FOREST:

The roofed oak tree canopy means that hostiles can spawn here, even in the daytime. So it's best to explore these from the rooftop instead.

LOOT AND TREASURE GUIDE
DESERT TEMPLES

If you find a desert temple, you're in luck as they contain four chests! The loot isn't very unique, but at least there's a lot of it!

Each chest can contain bones, rotten flesh, gunpowder, sand, string, gold ingots, spider eyes, iron ingots, emeralds, enchanted books, saddles, golden apples, iron horse armour, golden horse armour, diamonds, diamond horse armour and enchanted golden apples.

SWAMP:

Just like the roofed forests, hostiles can roam around in the daytime due to hanging vines and trees around the swamp. Witches live here and you might find a witch's hut. You'll also find blue orchids, lily pads and lots of stagnant pools of water.

JUNGLE:

Amazing tall redwood trees grow here, but the vegetation is dense and hard work, as are the hostiles. If you have the stamina they are a great resource for useful items. Cocoa beans to make cookies are a favourite. Also look out for ocelots – you can tame them.

BEACH:

These are found where an ocean biome meets another biome. A great place for a spot of fishing.

MUSHROOM ISLANDS:

This is a rare and unique biome, usually found in the ocean. Giant mushrooms grow here, as the name might suggest! They are a very safe place to set up a home.

Grow your own trees in caves!

ICE PLAINS:

Flat and covered in ice and snow – water freezes here instantly!
You might be lucky enough to spot a roaming polar bear.
Igloos can be found here and most contain loot.

ICE SPIKES:

Pretty much the same as the icy plains, except for one major thing.
Huge ice spikes spring from the earth up to 50 blocks high.

COLD TAIGA:

Similar to the taiga biome to the taiga biome below,
but with plenty of added snow!

COLD:

EXTREME HILLS:

Dramatic hills rise up from the ground in this cold biome that can flit
between snow and rain. Climb to the top of the hills for amazing views
into the distance – just don't fall! You'll love the llamas that spawn
here, but not so much the silverfish.

TAIGA:

A bit like the jungle in density, this biome is packed with
spruce trees and ferns! Villages are usually found here –
a great place to trade emeralds.

DID YOU KNOW?

Buried treasure will always be found along a shore and in the sand.

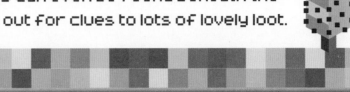

DESERT:

Full of sand and cacti and not much else – this is a very hard place to survive. Look out for villages, wells and temples. Some temples can even be found beneath the sand – so keep a look out for clues to lots of lovely loot.

SAVANNAH:

Very dry with no rainfall and lots of flat land. Here you'll find the odd village. Lots of horses and llamas roam the open space too.

MESA:

A rare biome that is made of clay. A beautiful place to explore, you might even find the real-life Bryce Canyon here. Abandoned mines litter the landscape where you can find lots of lovely gold.

OCEAN AND DEEP OCEAN:

The ocean biomes make up 60% of the game's surface. Get around by swimming or building your very own boat. There is lots of food here and plenty to find and explore, including shipwrecks, temple ruins and buried treasure. Just watch out for hostiles who can pack a real punch, especially if they are armed with a trident.

TOP DISCOVERIES

When out exploring, what have you discovered so far that's been truly awesome? Maybe a combo of materials and equipment that had an unexpected effect? Perhaps an action that helped you learn something new? **Complete the boxes below with your top findings.**

BEST ARMOUR/WEAPON COMBO YOU'VE DISCOVERED:

....

....

BEST ACCIDENTAL DISCOVERY:

....

....

BEST GEM STASH DISCOVERY:

....

....

BEST DISCOVERY THAT TAUGHT YOU A VALUABLE LESSON:

....

....

BEST DISCOVERY THAT LED TO A GAMEPLAY SECRET:

....

....

BEST DISCOVERY THAT STILL LEAVES YOU BAFFLED:

....

....

A DISCOVERY YOU WISH YOU HAD NEVER ENCOUNTERED:

....

....

ODD BLOCK OUT

Circle the item below that is different from the rest.

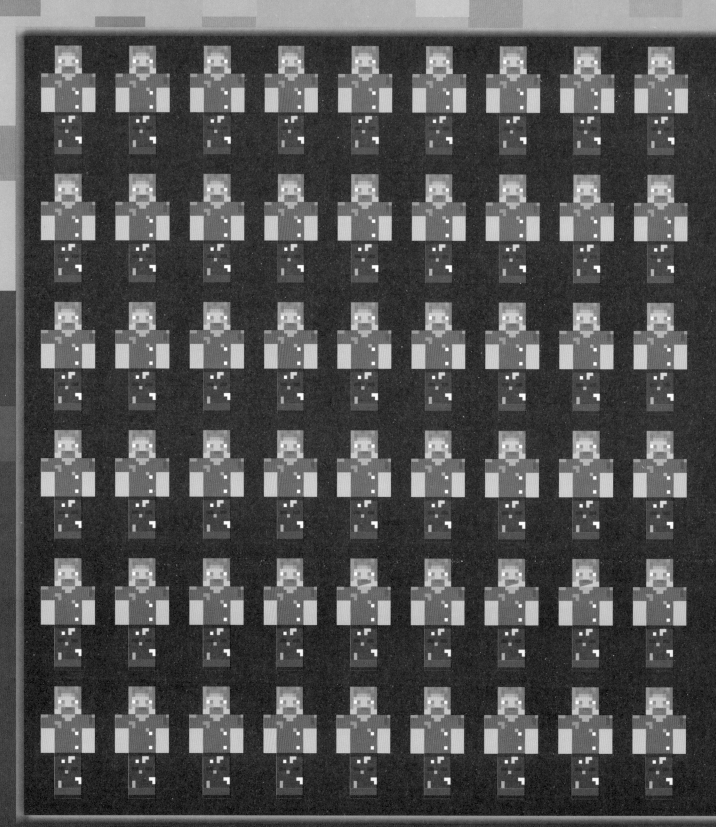

TOP TIP!

Don't bother making gold tools – no durability.

In abandoned mines, you'll occasionally find abandoned chest minecarts. These act the same as normal treasure chests and contain torches, rails, coal, lapis lazuli, redstone, bread, iron ingots, beetroot seeds, melon seeds, pumpkin seeds, activator rails, detector rails, powered rails, name tags, gold ingots, golden apples, diamonds, enchanted books, iron pickaxes and enchanted golden apples.

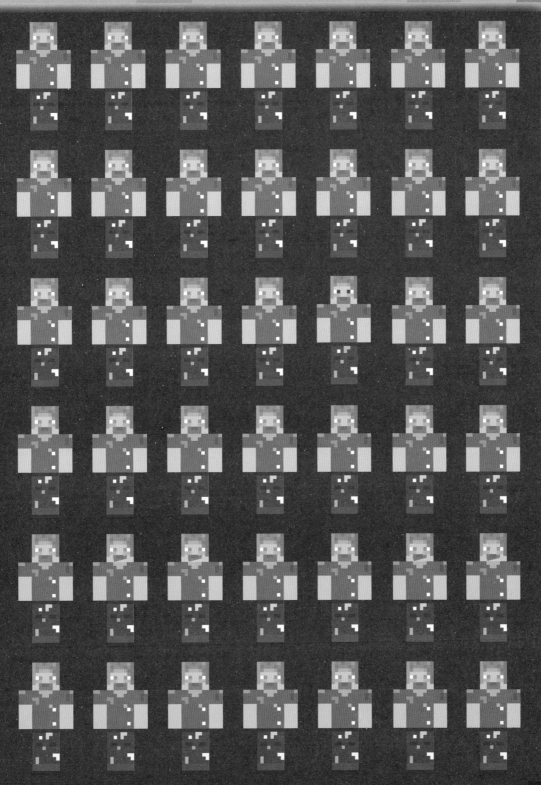

Answer on **PAGE 75**

53

WOODLAND MANSION CREATE

Using the grid below colour in the pixels to create
a secret-filled woodland mansion.

MINI BUILDS

FIREPLACE

YOU NEED: Slabs, iron bars, paintings, plant pots, flowers, Netherrack, flint and steel

A fireplace will brighten up any room. Use slabs to build the frame, and place railings in front as a fire guard. Netherrack burns forever, so use that as the "fuel"!

SOFA

YOU NEED: Stairs, trapdoors

To make a sofa, put two stair blocks next to one another, then put trapdoors at either end so that when you open them they sit alongside the blocks to form armrests.

GRANDFATHER CLOCK

YOU NEED: Dark oak bark, item frames, shovel, stick, clock

Use bark blocks to build a tall post, then, using item frames, attach a clock face to the top. Put a stick in the middle and a shovel below to look like a pendulum – you'll have to rotate them both to line up!

CURTAINS

YOU NEED: Banners

Fairly simple: just attach two banners to the top of a window to create a pair of curtains – they'll attach to glass panes without any problem!

 # LOOT AND TREASURE GUIDE

WOODLAND MANSIONS

These huge, mysterious buildings can contain chests in a number of spots, but each one has the same chance of containing the same items: gunpowder, string, bone, rotten flesh, wheat, coal, redstone dust, pumpkin seeds, melon seeds, beetroot seeds, iron ingots, bread, leads, name tags, gold ingots, diamond hoes, music discs ("Cat" and "13"), golden apples, buckets, chainmail chestplate, enchanted books, diamond chestplates and enchanted golden apples.

GREATEST ACHIEVEMENTS!

What are your greatest achievements so far as a player?
It's time to show them off! It could be creative, exploration,
or survival related. **Write down your top three below.**

Out of the three, which one are
you most proud of and why?

1

....

....

....

....

....

2

....

....

....

....

....

MINI BUILDS

PLANTER

YOU NEED: Dirt, trapdoors, a plant

Surround a dirt block with trapdoors, then open them to
create a large wooden planter. Now put in your plant!

LOOT AND TREASURE GUIDE

DUNGEONS

These small chambers containing monster spawners can have up to two chests. The loot inside is a selection of bones, rotten flesh, gunpowder, string, wheat, coal, redstone dust, beetroot seeds, melon seeds, pumpkin seeds, iron ingots, bread, name tags, saddles, gold ingots, golden apples, music discs ("13" or "Cat"), buckets, iron horse armour, enchanted books, gold horse armour, diamond horse armour and enchanted golden apples.

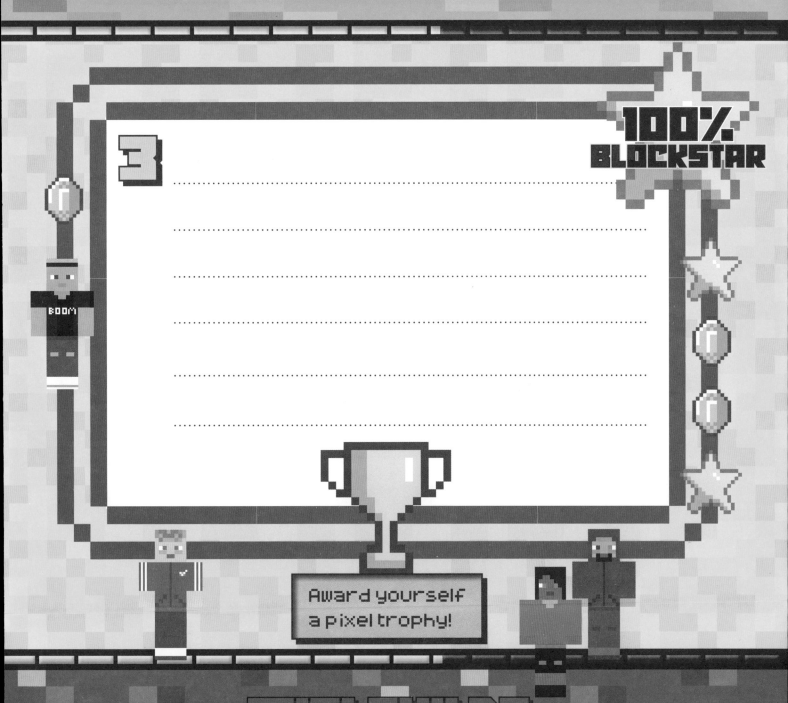

3

100%
BLOCKSTAR

Award yourself
a pixel trophy!

MINI BUILDS

FLOOR LAMP

YOU NEED: End rods , plant pot

Stack two End rods on top of each other, then put a plant pot on the top to look like a lampshade.
The End rods will be emitting the light, but it looks like a free-standing floor lamp!

BLOCK DREAMER

Imagine you had endless resources available and you could build your dream house! Map out a floor plan on the grid below with your sticker blocks. Label all the features and secrets you would hide inside. **Get dreaming, then get building!**

Materials wish list

....

....

Room wish list

....

....

....

....

COMPUTER

YOU NEED:
Stairs, activator rail, painting

Stick a painting to the back of any stair block to act as the screen, and an activator rail in front to be the "keyboard".

Secrets wish list

....

....

PORTAL PARTY

You may have used portals to travel to other realms, but where would you portal to if you could create your own realm?
Who would you invite to play with you?

Where does your portal go?
Describe the realm below.

....
....
....
....
....
....
....
....
....
....
....
....
....
....
....

Things to think about: climate, enemies, structures, nature, resources

Who would you invite to play with you?

1. .... 2. .... 3. ....

4. .... 5. .... 6. ....

DESIGN A NEW PORTAL DOOR

100 CREATIVE BUILDS

You'll never get stuck for build ideas ever again with this fun list. Close your eyes, hover your hand above the book, then randomly drop a finger onto the page and see where it lands. **That is your next build!**

AIRPLANE

ABANDONED CITY

Airport

BUS

Animal Shelter

....

APARTMENT BUILDING

ARCADE

BOWLING ALLEY

SKATEPARK

BATTLE ARENA

BARBER SHOP

Beaches

Electronic STORE

CASTLE

CONTAINER SHIP

Basketball Court

DANCE STUDIO

....

CHOCOLATE FACTORY

Box Factory

FASHION SHOW RUNWAY

FILM SET

HOTEL

CHAMBER FOR ENEMIES

FOOTBALL PITCH

....

GLASS PALACE

Helicopter

SHOPS

....

LABORATORY

CAMPSITE

Ice Cream van

Tennis COURT

Stables

BLACKSMITH

CLOTHES STORE

Community Garden

DINER

COLOSSEUM

....

FOUNTAIN

COTTAGES

MINESHAFT

GAMING CAFE

RAWR!

DINOSAUR

DOCK

SUBURBIA

GIANT COMPUTER

GOLF COURSE

Farm LIBRARY

Add more ideas to this page and fill it up to bursting!

SKYSCRAPER Sky Diving Scene POOL

....

SNOW FORTRESS

Hockey

Lighthouse OFFICE BLOCK

THEATRE

SWAMP SAUNA

UNDERGROUND TRAIN

MAZE Mud Pit

....

MERRY-GO-ROUND UNDERWATER CITY SPAS

OBSTACLE COURSE TEMPLE RUIN POWER PLANT

....

TOY SHOP Prison

Racetrack RAPIDS RIDE Hang Glider

RESTAURANT

PIZZA PARLOR RETIREMENT VILLA SKI HILL

Lemonade Stand

Playground ROLLER COASTER School SKATING RINK

POWER PLANT ROYAL KINGDOM ZOO OUTDOOR STAGES

BAKERY ROLLER SKATING RINK

....

Paintball Arena Snowball Fight Arena WATER SPORTS WALKING TRAILS

PETTING ZOO TRAMPOLINE WINTER LODGE

TABLE TENNIS TABLE

Stadium SAWMILL (WITH WATER WHEEL) YOUR REAL LIFE HOUSE

JAPANESE TRADITIONAL GARDEN OLYMPIC SWIMMING POOL

....

63

ENCOUNTERS OF THE BLOCK KIND

You meet all sorts when you're out and about! Some good, some bad and some neutral (you never know what mood they are in!). **Write about your favourite encounters under each category below.**

Favourite friendly animal encounter:

....
....
....
....

Favourite neutral animal encounter:

....
....
....
....

Favourite villager encounter:

....
....
....
....

Favourite hostile encounter:

....
....
....
....

DID YOU KNOW? >>>>>>>>>>>>>>>>>>

Underwater temples glow underwater to make them easier to spot.

TOP TIP!

Make a shield to fight skeletons.

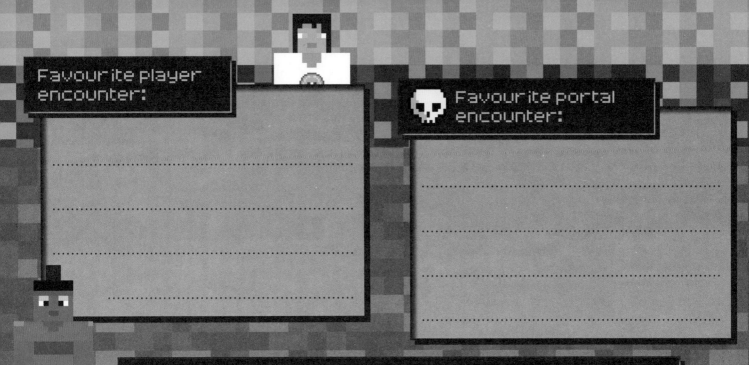

Favourite player encounter:

....

....

....

Favourite portal encounter:

....

....

....

....

Doodle your favourite block encounter of all in the box:

A TO Z

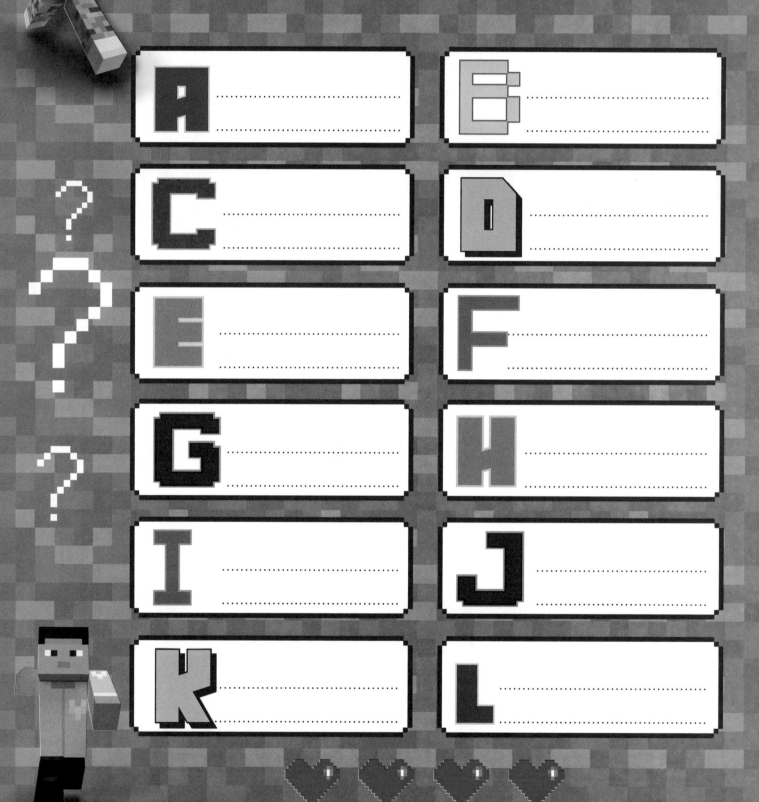

A ....
....

B ....

C ....

D ....

E ....

F ....

G ....

H ....

I ....

J ....

K ....

L ....

DID YOU KNOW?

Dolphins can lead to shipwrecks and temples.

M ....

N ....

O ....

P ....

Q ....

R ....

S ....

T ....

U ....

V ....

W ....

X ....

Y ....

Z ....

? ? ? ? ?

TOP TIP! Iron is probably the best multipurpose ore, so mine lots of it.

67

THE BIG BLOCK QUIZ

Take this quiz to find out if you really know the game!

1 WHICH ONE OF THESE CAN YOU TRADE WITH IN THE MINECRAFT GAME?

    a   A pig
    b   A villager
    c   A skeleton

2 WHICH ONE OF THESE WAS THE ORIGINAL NAME FOR THE MINECRAFT GAME?

    a   Block Buddies
    b   Cave Game
    c   Go Pickaxe!

3 WHICH YEAR WAS THE MINECRAFT GAME RELEASED?

    a   2009
    b   2010
    c   2011

4 WHICH OF THESE IS NOT FOUND IN THE MINECRAFT GAME?

    a   Panda
    b   Owl
    c   Turtle

5 HOW BIG IS THE MINECRAFT CRAFTING GRID?

    a   3x3
    b   4x4
    c   5x5

TOP TIP! As soon as you can, make yourself some potions.

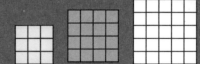

6. HOW MANY STICKS DO YOU NEED TO MAKE A SWORD IN MINECRAFT?

a   1
b   2
c   3

7. WHAT'S THE MOST COMMON ORE IN MINECRAFT?

a   Emerald
b   Diamond
c   Iron

8. WHAT'S THE RAREST ORE IN MINECRAFT?

a   Emerald
b   Diamond
c   Iron

9. WHICH BLOCK DO YOU USE TO COOK THINGS WITH IN MINECRAFT?

a   Stove
b   Furnace
c   Campfire

10. WHAT DO YOU NEED TO TAME AN OCELOT IN MINECRAFT?

a   Raw Fish
b   Carrot
c   Egg

Answer on PAGE 76

FAN FICTION

Have you read any of the fan fiction stories out there? Why not try writing your own adventure story? It can be completely made up or based on your real life game experience.
If you're stuck for inspiration then pick three words from the box below and use them to create your gaming tale.

Fight, Survival, Attack, Friendship, Night, Dungeon, Mansion, Torch, Ruin, Temple, Cold, Hot, Secret Village, Dragon, Treasure

....

....

....

....

....

....

....

....

....

MINI BUILDS

DESK LAMP

YOU NEED: Sea lantern, trapdoors, fence post

Surround a sea lantern (or any glowing block) with trapdoors (except on the bottom) and place a fence post underneath to create a desk lamp.

MY THREE WORDS ARE:

....

....

....

....

....

....

....

....

....

....

....

....

BLOCK 'N' ROLL

....

....

....

....

EAT. SLEEP. MINE. REPEAT.

JOKES

LOL!

WHAT DID the MINECRAFTER SAY WHEN SHE SAW HER HOUSE HAD BEEN FILLED WITH VEGETABLES?
There's not mush-room in here!

WHERE DID THE CREEPER FINISH IN THE RUNNING RACE?
In blast place!

HA HA

LOL!

KNOCK KNOCK!
WHO'S THERE?
THE INTERRUPTING CREEPER!
THE INTERRUPTING CREE....
BOOOOOOOOOOOOOOOOOOOOOOM

WHY WAS THERE A TRAFFIC JAM IN MINECRAFT?
Because of the road block!

WHY SHOULDN'T YOU TAKE THE ENDER DRAGON TO SEE A FILM?
Because he'll only be there for the end!

100% UNOFFICIAL
MINECRAFTERS
UNITE

© Centum

100% UNOFFICIAL
MINECRAFTERS UNITE

© Centum

ANSWERS

PAGE 12:

PAGE 35:

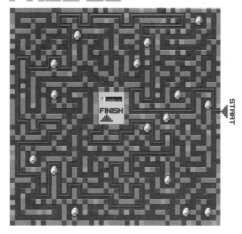

PAGE 13:

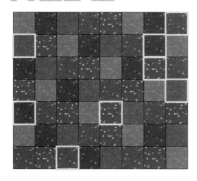

PAGES 38 – 39:

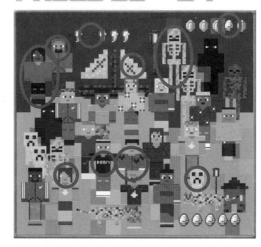

PAGE 32:

Across: 2. biome,
5. heart, **6.** furnace,
8. creative, **9.** spawn.
Down: 1. portal,
3. helmet, **4.** bedrock,
7. pickaxe, **9.** skin.

PAGES 44–45:

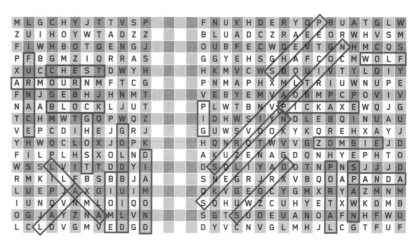

PAGE 33:

A = 6, **B** = 8,
C = 4, **?** = 18.

PAGE 34:

1. Wood block,
2. Emerald, **3.** Iron Ore,
4. Gold Ore.

PAGES 52–53:

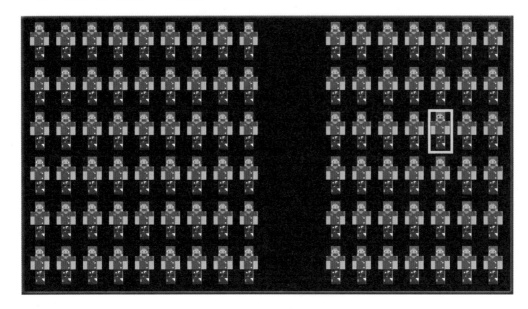

PAGES 68 – 69:

1. b, 2. b, 3. c, 4. b, 5. a,
6. a, 7. c, 8. a, 9. b, 10. a.

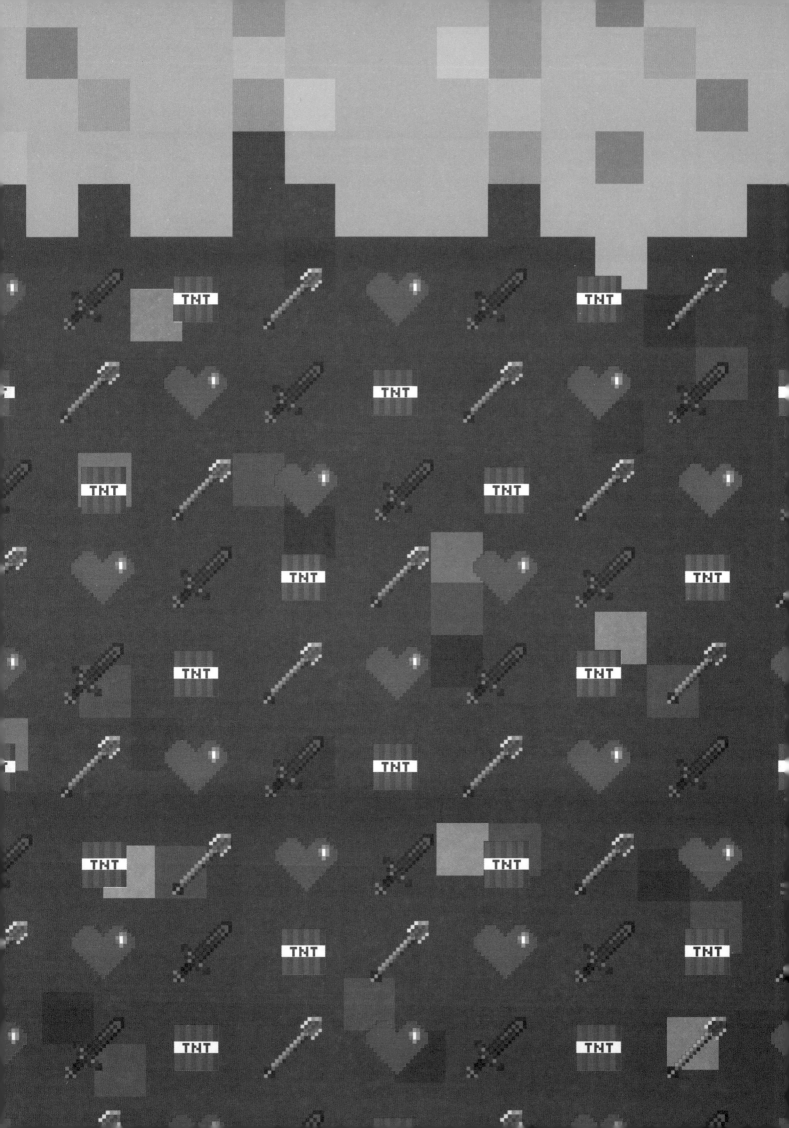